I DO.

WHEN THE GAME IS *RED* AND THE *STAKES* NEVER HIGHER...

ESPECIALLY NOW I DO.

"CHEETAH'S *CRIMES* CANNOT BE *DENIED.*

"STANDING WITH THE *LEGION OF DOOM.*

"THE *MURDER* OF APHRODITE.

"SHE IS LOST.

SHE THREATENS MY FELLOW *AMAZONS* AND THE VERY GODS WE CHAMPION...

ALL IN *MY* NAME, TO REPAY SOME *IMAGINED* DEBT SHE'S BEEN *MANIPULATED* INTO SEEING.

SHE *LASHES OUT,* DESPITE MY *CONSTANT* EFFORTS.

AND I... I MUST *CARE,* HONOR.

I *HAVE* TO. BUT...

"...I MUST *REMEMBER* HER."

HA! YOU MAY WIELD THE *GOD KILLER*, BEAST! BUT I WILL *NOT* SIMPLY *BEND* THE KNEE!

MUST I FIGHT *FOR* YOU, DIANA? ARE YOU *NOT* OUR *CHAMPION*?

LOOK HOW YOU *TALK* TO HER. YOU'RE ONLY *PROVING* MY POINT, HERA.

EVEN *YOU* CAN'T HIDE FROM THE TRUTH.

WHAT? YOU THINK THE *LASSO* WILL HOLD ME--?

I'LL *STRANGLE* YOU WITH IT! YOU--

THWIP

GOD OR ANIMAL...

GOOD FOR *YOU*, PRINCESS. YOU GOT YOUR *LASSO*...

I GOT TIME TO *RELOAD*.

DAMN THE LASSO!

BAM BAM

I *STILL* HOLD THE *GOD KILLER!*

SHRICK

HENGK!

MORE THAN ENOUGH BLADE FOR YOUR *GUT*, ASSASSIN!

CLICK CLICK

COME THEN, HERA! DIANA MAY STILL *WORSHIP* YOU...

BUT WHILE I HOLD THIS BLADE, YOU WILL *NEVER* MENACE HER--

--*AGAIN?!*

THWIP

NO! NOT WHEN I'M *THIS* CLOSE!

THWIP

THWIP

RELEASE ME!

ONLY *YOU* CAN DO THAT, BARBARA ANN...

YOU'VE **BECOME** WHAT YOU **HATE** MOST.

LIKE OUR **PATRONS,** YOU **CLAIM** KNOWLEDGE AND ASSISTANCE.

WHEN IN **TRUTH,** YOU **LORD** OVER OUR OWN CHOICES. **IGNORE US.**

DON'T YOU **SEE?**

IN YOUR RIGHTEOUS FURY TO **FREE** ME FROM THE GODS...

...YOU'VE **ALL** BUT **BECOME** ONE, BARBARA ANN.

I...**DID** WANT TO HELP. I DIDN'T WANT IT TO BE **TRUE...**

...BUT I'VE **FAILED** YOU, DIANA...

...AND I **SUBMIT.**

THERE IS A WAY BACK TO **PEACE,** CHEETAH...

...AND WE WILL **FIND** IT.

SURE AS YOU **REMAIN** BARBARA ANN MINERVA, ARCHAEOLOGIST AND **TEACHER...**

...AND I REMAIN *DIANA, PRINCESS OF THEMYSCIRA.* BEARER OF THE NAME *TRUTHQUEEN...*

...AND YOUR *FRIEND.*

I SUBMIT TO *YOU...*YES--

--BUT *NOT--*

--TO THEM!

IGNORANT ANIMAL!

SCHNKT

SHUNK

NYRAGH!

SILENCER!

NEVER TO THEM...

*WHERE IS CHEETAH OFF TO? FIND OUT IN *JUSTICE LEAGUE!*

STAY *STILL*, HONOR. THE *WOUND* IS--

THROUGH AND THROUGH. I CAN *FEEL* IT.

BUT I *CAN'T* DISLODGE THE SWORD. I'VE TAKEN *WORSE* PAIN THAN *THIS*, PRINCESS.

SO HOW ABOUT YOU SHOW ME THAT *STRENGTH*...AND PULL THIS DAMN THING *OUT*.

AS YOU *WISH*.

SHLERGK

RYAGH!

SHE'S *GONE*... SHOULD'VE *LEFT* ME.

I PUT YOUR *LIFE* ABOVE CHEETAH'S *PUNISHMENT*...

...AS I WOULD *AGAIN*.

THIS *DISPLEASES* YOU, HERA?

I'D HAVE *HOPED* YOU COULD BE *TRUSTED* TO DEAL WITH THE *UMBRAGE* OF *MORTALS*.

AND YET, THE *ANIMAL* HAS ESCAPED TO FURTHER HER *FOOL'S* MISSION AGAINST ME.

CHEETAH'S HUNT FOR THE GODS IS *OVER*. I *FELT* IT WHEN WE WERE IN THE LASSO. BUT...SHE WAS *NOT* A FOOL.

I THINK, IN A WAY...

...*CHEETAH WAS RIGHT*.

THANK *YOU*, TO *YOU* AND *ALL* MY PATRONS.

YOU'VE *INSPIRED* ME, GIVEN ME *STRENGTH* AND *DIRECTION*.

BUT MY RECENT SETBACKS, LOSING SOME OF THOSE CLOSEST TO ME...THIS CHAOS THAT'S BECOME MY LIFE HAS SHOWN ME...

...I NEED TO *REFOCUS*. TO *REDEFINE*. MY *MISSION* MUST CONTINUE...

...BUT *NOT* UNDER YOUR GUIDANCE, OR *ANYONE* ELSE'S.

THE MISSION OF *WONDER WOMAN*...

...MUST BE *DEFINED* BY *WONDER WOMAN*.

I'VE BEEN PULLED IN *TOO MANY* DIRECTIONS. WHEN MY *TRUE COMPASS* SHOULD BE MY *HEART* ALONE.

THANK YOU, HERA. *AGAIN*. ALWAYS...

BUT I DO *NOT* NEED YOU *ANYMORE*.

...WE'LL SEE.

BIG MOMENT... GLAD I COULD BE HERE FOR IT...

YOU'RE HURT **WORSE** THAN YOU SAID, SILENCER. THE HALL OF JUSTICE HAS **MEDICAL PODS.**

ALTHEA, **CHIEF SURGEON** OF THE AMAZONS, COULD CLOSE YOUR WOUND WITHOUT A SCAR.

LET ME **HELP** YOU. **VIOLENCE** NEED NOT BE YOUR **ONLY** TOOL...

AMAZON SCIENCE CAN HEAL YOUR BODY...**AND** YOUR MIND.

HARD PASS, PRINCESS...

YOU **THINK** WHAT I DO IS WRONG. I **BELIEVE** IT'S RIGHT. **YOURS** IS **NOT** THE ONLY **TRUTH.**

YOUR MORALS AREN'T THE **ONLY** MORALS. **MINE** BEGIN AND END WITH PROTECTING MY **FAMILY.**

AT **FIRST** I THOUGHT YOU WERE AN **IDIOT.** BUT SEEING YOU WORK, I **RESPECT** YOUR WAYS...LEARN TO RESPECT MINE.

THIS WILL **CAUTERIZE** THE WOUND. I DON'T NEED **AMAZON SCIENCE,** DIANA...

I JUST NEED YOU TO **HOLD MY HAND.** AND **SQUEEZE.**

SIZZLE

CAREFUL...IF MY HUSBAND **GETS** THIS BOSTON GIG, I'LL BE HERE **FULL-TIME** WASTING BULLETS ON YOU.

NO **WASTE.** YOUR **WORDS...**

THERE'S A *RUMOR* YOU HAVE SOMETHING FOR ME, DIANA.

AND THANK YOU *AS WELL* FOR LETTING ME *STUDY* THIS WONDER-WOMAN'S TOOLS.

I MUST *SOON RETURN* PENG DEILAN'S GIFTS. BUT SOMEDAY, PERHAPS...SHE WILL RETURN *HERE* WITH ME.

I'LL *REMEMBER* HER IN THE *LIVING ORAL HISTORY* AS SHEPHERD. BUT AS FOR HER *COMING* HERE...

WE HAVE SEEN SUCH *VIOLENCE* SINCE THE PATH TO EARTH REOPENED.

TO SURVIVE THE WORLD WE *REJOINED*, I THINK...WE MUST *ADAPT* TO MEET IT.

NOT *EVERYTHING* FROM EARTH'S BEEN *BAD*, ORANA. I'VE LEARNED *SO MUCH* SINCE I CAME HERE.

I'M *EARNING* MY WEAPON... HAVE *YOU* CHOSEN *YOURS*, DIANA?

I HAVE.

THE SWORD OF *EXORISTOS*. AN EXILE, WHO *RECLAIMED* HER HONOR IN THE AMERICAN REVOLUTION. MAY HER *BLADE* REMIND YOU...

...WHO *LEFT* IN *REVOLT* TO CO-FOUND THE BANA-MIGHDALL. WIELD IT, AND KNOW...

ALWAYS QUESTION *POWER*.

YOU HONOR US. FROM TODAY FORTH, DIANA...YOU'LL CARRY YOUR *ANCESTORS* WITH YOU IN BATTLE.

SO YOU'RE *LEAVING*, THEN? BACK TO *BOSTON*?

SOON ENOUGH, MAGGIE...

"...BUT THERE IS *ONE THING* LEFT TO DO."

IN *ALL* MY LIFE, I'VE NEVER *CLIMBED* TO THIS ALTAR.

YOU ALWAYS SAID THIS PLACE WAS FOR YOU TO *COMMUNE* WITH YOUR PAST...

...*QUEEN HIPPOLYTA.*

AND NOW, AFTER SO LONG APART...I *SHARE* THAT *PAST* WITH YOU.

THESE BRACELETS ARE *MINE...* *SHATTERED* BY *HERAKLES* IN THE *UPRISING* THAT *FREED* THE *AMAZONS.*

THEY HELPED *LIBERATE* AND *LEAD* OUR PEOPLE. TODAY...

...THESE ARE NOW THE *STRONGEST* BRACELETS WORN BY *ANY* AMAZON.

ORANA TELLS ME YOU'VE *REFOCUSED* YOUR MISSION ON YOUR *OWN* TERMS. AS *QUEEN,* I WORRY...

THEY'VE BEEN **BROKEN** FOR SO LONG.

SINCE BEFORE I **DREAMED** OF YOU, DIANA...ARE YOU **READY** TO BEGIN?

I AM.

WE **REFORGE** THEM.

AS **MOTHER** AND **DAUGHTER.**

AND THE **METAL** BONDING THE SHARDS?

AMAZONIUM. FOUND DEEP IN THE ISLAND BY OUR GEOLOGIST, DOTSIA. ONCE BROKEN...

BUT AS YOUR **MOTHER**...I COULD NOT BE **PROUDER.**

DO YOU NOT WISH TO **KNOW** THE MISSION?

AS **IF** I DON'T...

SINCE WE BROKE OUR **CHAINS,** WE'VE BEEN **REBELS.** SINCE I NAMED YOU, YOU'VE BEEN A **HUNTER.**

AND THAT **HUNT,** THAT **MISSION,** MORE THAN EVER...

ART BY TRAVIS MOORE & TAMRA BONVILLAIN

HELLO? THE FIRE DEPARTMENT IS ON THE WAY.

IS ANYONE STILL *IN* THERE?

WHO'S THAT LITTLE GIRL? SHE'S GOT TO GET *OUT* OF THERE!

SHE KNOWS WHAT SHE'S DOING, MA'AM.

GOD IN HEAVEN, I HOPE SHE KNOWS WHAT SHE'S DOING.

OKAY! LOOK, I'M GONNA... I'M GONNA DO A *THING*, ALL RIGHT?

YOU KIDS LIKE SLIDES?

YOU'RE GONNA HAVE TO HELP YOUR MAMA DOWN, OKAY?

THIS IS GOING TO WORK.

I THINK THIS IS GOING TO WORK.

I HOPE THIS WORKS.

I *TOLD* YOU IT WAS GOING TO WORK!

SPLSH

SHE... SHE DID IT. HOW DID SHE...WHO *IS* SHE?

SHE'S STAR-BLOSSOM.

SHE'S MY *DAUGHTER.*

GO *AGAIN,* MOMMY!

THE BUILDING'S GOING TO *COLLAPSE.* THERE ARE STILL PEOPLE ON THE FIRST *FLOOR!*

THE EXITS ARE ALL *BLOCKED!* YOU HAVE TO *HELP* THEM!

UM.

I'LL *TRY!*

I CAN SMOTHER THE *FIRE,* BUT...

...WHAT DO I DO *NOW?*

RESPECTFULLY, PRINCESS OF THE BOUQUET...

...PERHAPS I MIGHT BE ALLOWED TO ASSIST?

THIS MUST ALL SEEM A LITTLE SILLY TO YOU, DIANA.

NO. I MISS MY HOME, MY FAMILY.

THIS IS THE NICEST EVENING I'VE HAD IN SOME TIME.

OH! I JUST REMEMBERED!

I MADE YOU SOMETHING!

DON'T GO NOWHERE!

SHE'S NOT LIKE ANYONE ELSE, IS SHE?

NO. EVEN *BEFORE* HER MUTATION SHOWED.

SHE WAS ALWAYS HELPING SOMEONE.

PRINCESS, WE'VE BEEN READING A FAIR BIT. ABOUT THE TEEN TITANS.

LOTTA TRAGEDY FOLLOWED THOSE KIDS.

YES.

AND WITH HER HEART SO *OPEN...*

...I FEAR IT MIGHT *BREAK* UPON ENCOUNTERING WHAT'S OUT THERE.

THAT FAMILY TODAY, THEY'RE QUITE LIKELY ALIVE *BECAUSE* OF HER HEART.

WE CAN'T STOP HER. WE DON'T KNOW IF WE WANT TO *TRY.*

BUT WE HAVE A FAVOR TO ASK.

DIANA.

DAUGHTER.
I BRING SAD TIDINGS.

MOTHER?!

OSCAR AND YOLANDA MCGILL, THIS IS *HIPPOLYTA*, QUEEN OF THEMYSCIRA.

IT'S HOOKSWIFT, DAUGHTER. I'M SORRY.

SHE'S GONE.

HEY. HEY, WHAT'S GOING ON?

WHAT HAPPENED?

SHE FOUGHT, DIANA. UNTIL SHE COULD FIGHT NO MORE.

AND SHE WAS SURROUNDED BY THE TENDER AFFECTIONS OF ALL YOUR SISTERS.

FORGIVE ME, MY FRIENDS.

MY HOME, MY *ISLAND*... IT'S PROTECTED BY A CLAN OF GREAT SHARKS. *MEGALODONS*, YOU WOULD NAME THEM.

IT IS A TASK THEY CHOSE, OUT OF LOVE.

"THEY OPTED OUT OF IMMORTALITY. THEY FEEL ILLNESS, INJURY, AND THE SIMPLE, ENDLESS TURN OF THE CLOCK.

"I WAS THE ONLY CHILD... MY SISTERS, MANY, MANY CENTURIES OLDER.

SHE WAS MY... SHE WAS MY FRIEND.

FORGIVE ME.

I NEED MOMEN*

DIANA!

YOUR MAJESTY... MAYBE... MAYBE WE CAN GIVE THEM A MINUTE?

DO YOU LIKE BAKED MACARONI AND CHEESE, BY CHANCE?

I CONFESS, I AM *INTRIGUED.*

DIANA?

I THINK I NEED TO BE ALONE FOR A MOMENT, PLEASE, PEONY.

ME, TOO. YEP.

MAYBE THIS IS A BAD TIME TO GIVE YOU THIS.

OR MAYBE IT'S THE BEST TIME.

YOU EAT LIKE THIS EVERY DAY? IT'S... IT'S *REMARKABLE.*

HIPPOLYTA. WE WERE GOING TO ASK DIANA, BUT PERHAPS WE SHOULD ASK YOU *BOTH.*

WILL YOU WATCH OVER OUR DAUGHTER?

IF YOU WILL PROMISE TO WATCH OVER *MINE.*

SHE CAN BE QUITE IMPETUOUS, FROM TIME TO TIME.

MR. MCGILL, IF YOU PLEASE...?

ME?

I THOUGHT THIS WAS A *MOM* THING.

NO. IT'S WORRY. IT'S CARE.

IT'S A *PARENT* THING, OSCAR.

GODDESS. IT'S *BEAUTIFUL.*

I MADE IT IN YOUR COLORS! *SENIOR SOROR,* IT'S CALLED. IT MEANS--

"BIG SISTER."

LIKE HOOKSWIFT.

--DIANA. YOU DON'T ALWAYS HAVE TO BE THE WORLD'S BIG SISTER.

IT'S OKAY TO NOT BE *UNTOUCH-ABLE.*

...

WASN'T I SUPPOSED TO BE MENTORING *YOU?*

YOU ARE.

BIG SISTER.

WE SHOULD GET BACK. I MEAN, CAKE, RIGHT?

AND ALSO, I DON'T KNOW HOW OUR MOMS ARE GETTING ALONG.

TREMENDOUSLY WELL, I HOPE.

BECAUSE *MY MOTHER IS A HORRENDOUS COOK!*

From Small Things, Mama

GAIL SIMONE WRITER   COLLEEN DORAN ARTIST

HI-FI COLORIST   DAVE SHARPE LETTERER

BRITTANY HOLZHERR ASSOCIATE EDITOR   ALEX ANTONE EDITOR

ART BY EMANUELA LUPACCHINO & TOMEU MOREY

"WONDER WOMAN.

"WHAT'S SHE DOING HERE?"

THE INTERROGATION

writer MARIKO TAMAKI artist ELENA CASAGRANDE
colorist SUNNY GHO letterer ANDWORLD DESIGN
editor BRITTANY HOLZHERR group editor BRIAN CUNNINGHAM

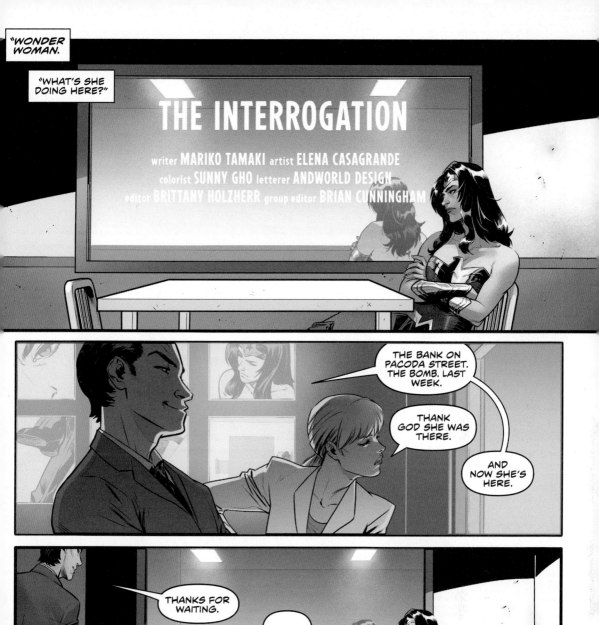

THE BANK ON PACODA STREET. THE BOMB. LAST WEEK.

THANK GOD SHE WAS THERE.

AND NOW SHE'S HERE.

THANKS FOR WAITING.

YES.

WONDER WOMAN. AM I SAYIN' THAT RIGHT?

IS THERE ANOTHER WAY TO SAY IT?

JUST BEIN' THOROUGH.

APPRECIATE YOU COMING IN. YOU KNOW WE'RE STILL SCRATCHING OUR HEADS OVER THESE BOMBINGS.

YES.

YES.

HORRIBLE THING.

I WON'T TAKE UP *TOO* MUCH OF YOUR TIME.

YOU KNOW, I ALWAYS WONDER, MYSELF, HOW YOU SUPERHERO TYPES DO IT.

DO WHAT?

GET THERE IN THE NICK OF TIME.

"WE DON'T."

"THAT'S RIGHT, ISN'T IT. BUT YOU DID SAVE SIX PEOPLE. PULLED THEM RIGHT OUT OF THE RUBBLE. THAT'S NOT NOTHING."

"NO. IT IS NOT."

WHICH BRINGS US TO...

...THIS MORNING.

"COULD'VE BEEN A DISASTER.

"BUT THERE YOU WERE. SAVING THE DAY.

"I IMAGINE IT HELPS TO GET THERE EARLY.

"IN THIS CASE, IN THE CROWD THREE HOURS BEFORE 'ACTION.'

"A BEACON IN HIDING.

"POTENTIAL TRAGEDY. ACTUAL TRAGEDY. THERE YOU ARE. *EVERY* TIME.

"GOT ME TO THINKING...

...WHAT'S THE DIFFERENCE BETWEEN A HERO...

THAT IS YOUR *WEAKNESS*, WONDER WOMAN.

YOU ARE BUT A COG IN MY MACHINE OF *DEATH* AND *DESTRUCTION*.

AND YOUR WEAKNESS...

...IS YOU THINK EVERYTHING IS ABOUT YOU.

WHAT?

THIS IS *MY* INTERROGATION, *ARES*.

NOT YOURS.

THE END

ART BY JOSÉ LUIS GARCÍA-LÓPEZ & TRISH MULVIHILL

ART BY BILQUIS EVELY & MAT LOPES

NEW ORLEANS, THE FRENCH QUARTER.
MARDIS GRAS.

HEY, YOU **MADE** IT!

NICE TO KNOW THAT AT 4,727 YEARS OLD I CAN **STILL** BE SURPRISED.

HONEST TO HECATE, I DIDN'T THINK YOU WOULD...

...THAT **SECOND** GLASS IS FOR **YOU**, BY THE WAY.

THE **CHAMPAGNE** IS EXCELLENT, YOU SHOULD **REALLY** HAVE A TASTE.

NO, THANK YOU, CIRCE.

I CAME TO TALK **BUSINESS**, NOT TO **CELEBRATE** FAT TUESDAY.

♪ ...NOT SO LONG AGO, IN NEW ORLEANS, LOUISIANA, NAMED MARIE LAVEAU-- ♪

CIRCE.

♪ --BELIEVE IT OR NOT, STRANGE AS IT SEEMS, SHE MADE A FORTUNE SELLING VOODOO AND INTERPRETIN' DREAMS-- ♪

♪ --MHM HELPED THEM, IN HER HAND, NEW ORLEANS WAS HER PROMISE LAND-- ♪

♪ --QUALITY FOLKS CAME FROM FAR AND NEAR-- ♪

CIRCE.

♪ --THIS WONDER WOMAN FOR TO HEAR... ♪

...I DON'T WORK FOR FREE, DI.

KINDA FLIES IN THE FACE OF THE WHOLE IN-IT-FOR-MYSELF LIFESTYLE, Y'KNOW?

I WILL PAY YOU. I HAVE MONEY.

SO DO I, BABY.

I DON'T NEED MONEY.

GIG LIKE THIS, IT'S GOT TO BE SOMETHING PRECIOUS.

IT'S GOT TO BE SOMETHING THAT HURTS.

YOU'RE SAYING YOU CAN DO IT?

IT'S POSSIBLE?

MAGIC, BABY, AND *I'M* THE MOST POWERFUL WITCH IN *EXISTENCE*...

...WELL, EXCEPT MAYBE FOR ZATANNA. STUCK-UP BRAT. "OOOH, THAT'S *IMMORAL!*" BAH.

ANYTHING IS *POSSIBLE* WITH THE RIGHT *WILL* AND FOR THE *RIGHT PRICE.*

YOU JUST GOTTA BE WILLING TO *PAY,* PRINCESS.

ARE YOU?

I *CANNOT* ANSWER THAT UNTIL I KNOW WHAT YOU *ASK.*

WE'RE TALKING *BIG* MAGIC. WE'RE TALKING *STICKING-IT-TO-A-GOD* MAGIC.

THAT'S *EXPENSIVE.* THAT REQUIRES YOU *GIVING SOMETHING OF YOURSELF.*

SOMETHING *PRECIOUS.* SOMETHING THAT *HURTS* TO GIVE *UP.*

OH, AND *LOOK...*

...YOU BROUGHT IT *WITH* YOU...

...I THINK YOU HAVE HAD ENOUGH.

YOU! ALWAYS YOU!

WHY WON'T YOU LEAVE ME ALONE?

YOU KNOW WHY.

YOU'RE MY FRIEND.

I LOVE YOU. I WILL NEVER ABANDON YOU.

GRRRRRRTHEN LET OURRR FRRRIENDSHIP--

RRRROOOWWWRRRULL MRRROWR RRRRRR...

SHE *REALLY* IS NOT HAPPY.

ARE YOU READY TO BEGIN?

ALMOST.

OUT LET ME OUT...

IT'S NOT THAT I DON'T *TRUST* YOU TO HONOR THE DEAL, DI.

BUT WE NEED TO COMPLETE OUR BUSINESS *FIRST*.

...OUT FRRREEE ME...

THIS IS THE *HOLY OF HOLIES* TO MY PEOPLE, CIRCE.

IF IT WILL *FREE* BARBARA ANN FROM WHAT *TORMENTS* HER, I WILL GIVE IT *GLADLY*.

THEN IN RETURN, I WILL *RESTORE* HER.

--AFFLICTED, ACCURSED, ACCURSE'D--

--CHAINED, TETHERED, AND BOUND--

--SHE WHO SEEKS TO BREAK THE BONDS OF A VILE GOD--

--SHE WHO SEEKS TO BE AS SHE WAS BEFORETIMES--

--SHE WHO SEEKS TO BE FREE OF THE CURSE URZKARTAGA HAS SET UPON HER--

--SPEAK THE WORDS AND BE AS YOU WERE--

--SPEAK THE NAME OF BARBARA ANN MINERVA OF THY OWN WILL, FROM THY OWN LIPS--

--SPEAK THY NAME AND THAT YE SHALL BE!

PLEASE.

PLEASE, BARBARA ANN, JUST SAY THE WORDS...

...JUST SAY YOUR NAME...

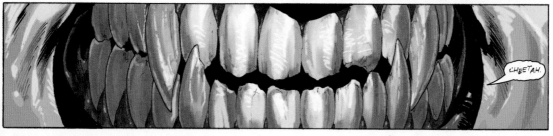

CHEETAH.

SO, I SENT HER **BACK** TO HER LITTLE **TEMPLE** IN THE **JUNGLE**.

YOU SHOULD DRINK THIS. MAYBE SOME **WINE** THAT REMINDS YOU OF **HOME** WILL HELP.

YOU CAN HAVE THAT **BACK**. I FAILED TO HOLD UP MY END OF THE DEAL.

YOU DID **NOT**. SHE **REFUSED**. YOU DID AS YOU **PROMISED**.

IS SHE RESTORED? NOPE. SHE'S AS SHE **ALWAYS** WAS, ALWAYS **WILL BE**.

WHY ARE YOU BEING **KIND** TO ME?

BECAUSE IT PLEASES ME TO BE KIND RIGHT NOW. AND BECAUSE IT'S NO FUN KICKING SOMEONE WHEN THEY'RE **DOWN**.

ALL SHE HAD TO DO WAS SAY HER NAME, CIRCE. THAT WAS **ALL** SHE HAD TO **DO**.

YOU **STILL** DON'T GET IT, NOT EVEN AFTER ALL THESE **YEARS** IN THE WORLD OF MEN.

WHY SOMEONE WOULD **CHOOSE** TO DO THE ABSOLUTELY **WRONG** THING, **KNOWING** IT WAS THE WRONG THING TO **DO**.

NO, I DO NOT. IT MAKES NO SENSE.

THE **HEART** RARELY **DOES**.

I WILL TRY **AGAIN**.

I KNOW.

N**EVER** C**HANGE**

Greg RUCKA writer

Nicola SCOTT artist

Romulo FAJARDO JR. colors

Rob LEIGH letters

Andrea SHEA associate editor

Mike COTTON editor

Brian CUNNINGHAM group editor

END

MY MOTHER LOOKS EXACTLY THE SAME. HOW WILL I LOOK IN TWO HUNDRED YEARS?

AMAZONIAN HISTORY? YOU MUST KNOW THAT BOOK BY HEART, DIANA.

WHAT IS THE WORLD LIKE BEYOND THEMYSCIRA, MOTHER?

LIKE THIS.

PLAGUED BY GREED, CRUELTY, AND PAIN. I'M GRATEFUL YOU WILL NEVER EXPERIENCE IT.

MAYBE I'M NOT.

BUT SHE DOESN'T HAVE TO WONDER WHAT'S OUT THERE.

MOTHER WOULD NEVER UNDERSTAND IF SHE KNEW HOW OFTEN I TRY TO IMAGINE A PLACE SHE WANTS TO FORGET.

I'M THE ONLY AMAZON WHO HAS SPENT HER ENTIRE LIFE ON THEMYSCIRA--THE ONLY ONE WHO HAS NO CHOICE BUT TO IMAGINE.

DIANA! COME SPAR WITH ME.

TO LEAVE PARADISE...

KAMI GARCIA WRITER
PHIL HESTER PENCILLER
ANDE PARKS INKER
TRISH MULVIHILL COLORIST
GABRIELA DOWNIE LETTERER
ANDREA SHEA ASSOCIATE EDITOR
BRITTANY HOLZHERR EDITOR
BRIAN CUNNINGHAM GROUP EDITOR

NUBIA IS RIGHT. MY LIFE IS PERFECT.

I SHOULD BE SATISFIED.

WHY AM I SO RESTLESS?

EVERYTHING I NEED IS HERE. THIS IS WHERE I BELONG.

ISN'T IT?

SO I DID SOME PONDERING--

--THERE'S ALWAYS SOMETHING GOING ON, SOMEONE NEEDING ME--

ALWAYS. IT NEVER STOPS.

--BUT IT'S NOTHING MY *RUFFIAN* FRIENDS CAN'T HANDLE BY THEMSELVES FOR A FEW DAYS.

IT WOULD BE GOOD TO BE JUST DIANA AGAIN...

"...FOR A LITTLE WHILE."

The End.

LET'S GET THE BALL ROLLING.

SRACK!

OUR WORLD AIN'T THE ONE YOU KNOW.

1939 BULLDOZED INTO 1940, AND THE U.S. GOT OFF ITS *TUCHUS* AND GRABBED THAT BULL BY THE HORNS.

AND WHO RODE OUT TO GREET THE REICH?

WHY, THE BEST GALS FOR THE JOB.

"THE MISTRESS OF MAGIC, THE STARGIRL, THE HUNTRESS, RENEE MONTOYA, AND THE SPLENDID SHAZAM--

"--THEY CALLED US **Bombshells.**

BUT AS LEGENDS TWIST AND CHANGE LIKE A SATURDAY AFTERNOON RADIO SERIAL, THERE IS ONE AMONG US WHO WILL BURN ETERNAL, FOREVER KNOWN TO YOU, TO ME, AND TO ALL WHO COME AFTER--

--AS *THE* *Wonder Woman.*

MARGUERITE BENNETT WRITER   LAURA BRAGA ARTIST   ROMULO FAJARDO JR. COLORIST   WES ABBOTT LETTERER

STEVE TREVOR, AERIAL ACE.

I RODE A SMOKING, WOUNDED FIGHTER PLANE ALL THE WAY TO PARADISE.

I FELL FROM THE HEAVENS.

SHE ROSE FROM THE EARTH.

THEMYSCIRA, AMAZONIA, PARADISE ISLAND--IT WAS A HAVEN OF WARRIOR WOMEN, AND THERE SHE STOOD, THEIR PRINCESS.

OF HER FEROCITY, THERE HAS NEVER BEEN ANY DOUBT.

I'VE SEEN HER DRAG DRAGONS FROM THE SKY.

BUT NO MATTER HER FURY, HER POWER, HER STRENGTH...

...I KNEW HER FIRST AS A HEALER.

I WAS... HAUNTED, BY THE THINGS I HAD SEEN.

SHE STAYED WITH ME.

HELD ME IN MY NIGHTMARES.

SHE TAUGHT ME THAT SCARS ARE NOT SHAMES, AND ALL HEALING IS A JOURNEY.

SHE TAUGHT ME TO HEAL MYSELF.

FOR THAT, I'LL ALWAYS LOVE HER.

BEFORE I WAS **MERA, QUEEN OF ATLANTIS,** I WAS "MERA, THAT RED-HAIRED LITTLE WAIF WHO KEPT DIANA OUT SO LATE SHE MISSED SUPPER."

WE WERE GIRLS TOGETHER PLAYING IN THE SURF WHERE THE KINGDOM OF ATLANTIS MET THE QUEENDOM OF THEMYSCIRA.

WE RODE DOLPHINS, RACED HIPPOCAMPI, TRADED SKINS WITH SELKIES, AND DRANK RAIN FROM HURRICANE STORMS.

SHE WAS MY FIRST FRIEND AND FIRST LOVE, WHICH MAY SEEM SUCH A LITTLE THING, COMPARED TO ALL THAT DIANA GREW TO BE.

BUT COMING UP FROM THE DARKNESS OF MY PAST...FROM THE DEPTH OF PAIN FROM THE FAMILY AND BIRTHRIGHT THAT CAST ME OUT...

...WHAT A LITTLE THING IT IS TO LOVE ANOTHER AND FEEL HELD BY THEM IN RETURN.

WHAT A LITTLE THING, TO HOLD THE ENTIRE WORLD.

I KNEW THAT ONE DAY SHE WOULD LEAVE ME--

--WOULD LEAVE ALL OF PARADISE BEHIND.

ONE DOESN'T LEAVE A MAGNIFICENT PEARL TO LANGUISH IN DARKNESS.

A PERFECT SHIELD THAT NEVER SEES THE BATTLEFIELD WILL NEVER BE PERFECT.

WE CANNOT BE COMPLETE IF WE ARE KEPT FROM OUR TRUE PURPOSE.

I LEARNED TO LOVE BECAUSE OF HER, AND IT'S TRUE WHAT THEY SAY--

--IT REALLY IS THE ONLY THING THAT CAN SAVE THE WORLD.

THE SOVIET SUPERGIRL.

IN WAR, I LOST MY SISTER, STARGIRL, THE ONE I LOVED MORE THAN MY OWN LIFE, AND IN MY GRIEF, I LOST TOO THE WILL TO FLY.

DIANA WAS MY COMFORT AND MY COUNSELOR THEN--THE ONE WHO TAUGHT ME HOW TO HEAL.

"SOME SAY THERE IS A BETTER PLACE, A DISTANT COUNTRY, FAIR AND FREE, WHERE WE MEET IN REUNION, IN FORGIVENESS, IN UNDERSTANDING...

SHE TOLD ME THAT TO LOVE AND LOSE AND HURT AND HEAL WAS HUMAN...BUT I TOLD HER THAT WE WERE NOT HUMAN, SHE AND I.

"WHAT IS DEATH TO US?" I ASKED. "HOW DO WE GRIEVE?"

"KARA, MY SUPERGIRL...

"...SOME SAY THAT TO ALL THINGS, THERE IS A REASON--THAT EACH THING HAS ITS PLACE AND TIME AND PURPOSE, LIKE A NOTE OF MUSIC, RISING, FALLING, AND THEN GONE, FOR NOTES DO NOT ENDURE BEYOND THEIR MOMENT; TO BECOME CACOPHONY.

"BUT THIS TRUTH, I DO NOT KNOW.

"AND THOSE WHO HAVE LOVED US AND GONE BEFORE US MAKE A PLACE FOR US TO COME; AND THERE REST AT LAST.

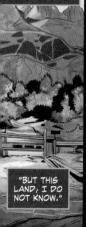

"BUT THIS LAND, I DO NOT KNOW."

"SOME SAY THERE IS A QUIET DARKNESS, AN EMBRACE IN THE BLACK, WITHOUT BURDEN, WITHOUT MEMORY...

AND THIS END GIVES SUCH A BRIGHTNESS TO WHAT CAME BEFORE, BECAUSE NOTHING SHALL COME AFTER.

"BUT THIS STILLNESS, I DO NOT KNOW.

"GRIEF MEANS SHE WAS *REAL*.

"GRIEF MEANS THAT SHE *MATTERED*.

"AS *YOU* MATTER. AS *THIS* MATTERS. AS IT *ALWAYS WILL*.

"IT WILL HURT TODAY, AND TOMORROW, AND *A YEAR* FROM NOW, AND *TEN YEARS* FROM NOW.

"IT MAY EVEN HURT *FOREVER*.

"BUT IT WILL NOT ALWAYS HURT THE SAME.

WHAT DO WE DO WITH GRIEF?

WE DO THE BEST WE CAN.

AND I WILL BE YOUR *FRIEND* FOR AS LONG AS YOU WILL HAVE ME.

AND I WILL BE HERE FOR YOU AS YOU DISCOVER *ALL THAT AWAITS*.

AND IN THAT MOMENT I THOUGHT, PERHAPS--

--I MAY HAVE THE STRENGTH TO *FLY*.

THE WONDER GIRLS!

WONDER WOMAN CHANGED THE WORLD--BUT EVEN SHE COULD NOT CHANGE HUMAN NATURE.

AFTER THREE YEARS OF WAR, AN AMERICAN PRESIDENT DELIVERED COMMANDS FROM ON HIGH--

--NOT WITH A SWORD, BUT WITH A *PEN*.

A *STAIN* TO MAKE A MARK TO LAST FOREVER.

EXECUTIVE ORDER 9066.

THE INTERNMENT OF JAPANESE-AMERICAN CIVILIANS.

WE CALLED FOR AID-- WE CALLED FOR WONDER WOMAN.

SHE AND HER FRIENDS HEARD OUR PLAN, AND CAME TO US IN THE DESERT.

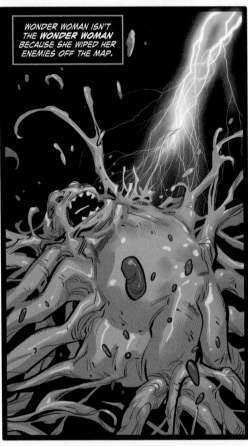

WONDER WOMAN ISN'T THE *WONDER WOMAN* BECAUSE SHE WIPED HER ENEMIES OFF THE MAP.

SHE DOESN'T HAVE ANY MORE ENEMIES BECAUSE SHE TURNS THEM INTO *FRIENDS*.

BUT WHAT SHE TAUGHT US WAS NOT LOVE, OR STRENGTH, OR HOW TO GRIEVE, OR HOW TO HEAL...

...SHE TAUGHT US OUR *OWN* MAGNIFICENT POWER.

WHAT WOULD YOU DO, KNOWING WHAT YOU KNOW NOW, *KNOWING WHAT YOU KNEW THEN?*

YOU HAVE YOUR CHANCES, AND YOUR CHOICES, AND THE GIFT OF YOUR LIFE.

BUT THE MOMENT TO *ACT*--

--TO MAKE SURE THAT *"NEVER AGAIN"* NEVER COMES AGAIN--

--THAT MOMENT IS ALWAYS, AND WILL ALWAYS BE--

"--RIGHT NOW."

DONNA TROY, CASSIE SANDSMARK, YUKI AND YURI KATSURA, AND EMILY SUNG--

--BECAUSE OF WONDER WOMAN, WE BECAME--

WONDER GIRLS!

WONDER GIRLS!

THE WONDER GIRLS!

THEY SAY I HAVE BEEN SO MANY THINGS TO THEM.
I NEVER MEANT TO BE.
BUT I AM GRATEFUL ALL THE SAME.
WHAT A LIFE I MIGHT HAVE HAD, A PRINCESS OF THEMYSCIRA...
...AND YET, NO MATTER THE WORLD, AND NO MATTER THE TIME...
...I THINK I WOULD ALWAYS CHOOSE, AND CHOOSE, AND CHOOSE AGAIN--
--I WOULD ALWAYS LEAVE PARADISE, AND GO INTO THE WORLD OF MORTALS, SUFFERING, AND PAIN...
...WHAT PURPOSE IS THERE BUT THIS?
TO TRY TO DO GOOD, BE GOOD, DO AND BE BETTER, AND KINDER, AND WISER THAN BEFORE?
I HAVE SEEN ALL I HAVE BEEN TO OTHERS.
WHAT AM I TO MYSELF?
I DO THIS BECAUSE I AM THIS.
I HOPE THAT IS ENOUGH.

MY NAME IS VANESSA KAPATELIS, AND I NEVER THOUGHT I WAS A BAD PERSON.

I ALWAYS ATE MY PEAS, ALWAYS LISTENED TO MY MOTHER, ALWAYS RECYCLED AND USED TURN SIGNALS.

DIANA?

I THOUGHT THAT WHEN THE GOING GOT TOUGH, I COULD HANDLE IT WITH GRACE.

AND I DID...

...UNTIL I BROKE.

WONDER WOMAN, DIANA PRINCE.

SHE SAVED MY LIFE, AND FOR A WHILE, SHE WAS MY *BEST FRIEND.*

THE DAY WE MET, I ALMOST DIED. I LOST THE USE OF MY LEGS, BUT SHE WOULDN'T LET ME GIVE UP. I HAD TO KEEP LIVING, SHE SAID. KEEP *FIGHTING.*

KLASH

I DECIDED TO TRY AN EXPERIMENTAL NANITE TREATMENT TO REPAIR MY SPINE.

I TAUGHT MYSELF TO *WALK* AGAIN BECAUSE SHE *BELIEVED* IN ME. I FELT *POWERFUL* AGAIN...

...AND THEN *I* TOOK THE NAME *SILVER SWAN* AND USED MY NEWFOUND POWER TO *BETRAY* HER.

Always

VITA AYALA WRITER
AMANCAY NAHUELPAN ARTIST
JAY DAVID RAMOS COLORIST
CLAYTON COWLES LETTERER
ANDREA SHEA EDITOR
BRIAN CUNNINGHAM GROUP EDITOR

OVER AND *OVER* AGAIN.

KA-CHCK

YOU'RE A *FRAUD*, WONDER WOMAN.

ENOUGH, VANESSA! *PLEASE.*

YOU DIDN'T *SAVE* ME THAT DAY YOU PULLED ME OUT FROM UNDER RUBBLE. YOU JUST WANTED TO LOOK LIKE A HERO FOR THE CAMERAS.

BUT AS SOON AS THE ADORING CROWD STOPPED WATCHING, YOU *ABANDONED* ME, AND NOW YOU HAVE TO DEAL WITH THE CONSEQUENCES.

I DIDN'T *ABANDON* YOU.

LIES! IF YOU'D *SHOWN UP* FOR ME, I WOULDN'T BE DOING ANY OF THIS. BUT YOU *DIDN'T.*

AND I FOUND MY *OWN WAY* TO BE STRONG WITHOUT YOU.

THIS BLOOD IS ON *YOUR HANDS.*

VANESSA...I WILL *ALWAYS* BE HERE WHEN YOU NEED ME. BUT YOU'RE NOT THE ONLY ONE WHO NEEDS MY HELP!

DON'T YOU DARE CALL ME THAT. *VANESSA* IS STILL WAITING FOR YOU TO COME BACK FOR HER.

I'M THE ONE WHO CRAWLED OUT OF THAT HOSPITAL ROOM WHEN I REALIZED YOU WERE NEVER SHOWING UP.

YOU BLAME ME FOR WHAT YOU'VE BECOME, BUT YOU'RE *WRONG.*

YOU ARE THE ONLY PERSON WHO CAN DECIDE YOUR ACTIONS.

IT WAS *YOU* WHO DECIDED TO LET YOUR *ANGER* RULE YOU.

IT WAS *YOU* WHO DECIDED TO HURT *INNOCENT PEOPLE.*

SHE WAS RIGHT.

SHE'S *ALWAYS* RIGHT.

I'M *TIRED* OF THIS GAME.

O-OH GOD, NO! *STAY AWAY!*

TIME TO SKIP TO THE END.

HURTING THEM WILL NOT GET YOU WHAT YOU WANT, VANESSA.

YOU HAVE A CHOICE RIGHT NOW. ONE THAT I CAN'T MAKE FOR YOU.

SHE WAS TELLING THE TRUTH.

I HAD TO MAKE A CHANGE.

PLEASE... I DON'T WANT TO BE THIS WAY ANYMORE, BUT I'M NOT STRONG ENOUGH TO...

YES YOU *ARE.*

IT WAS UP TO *ME* TO STOP TAKING THINGS OUT ON INNOCENT PEOPLE.

THE NANITES ARE GONE NOW. I HAVE THERAPY EVERY DAY...FOR MY BODY *AND* MY ANGER.

AND I *DESERVE* TO BE EXACTLY WHERE I AM.

HERE. *ALONE.*

CREEEEEEAK

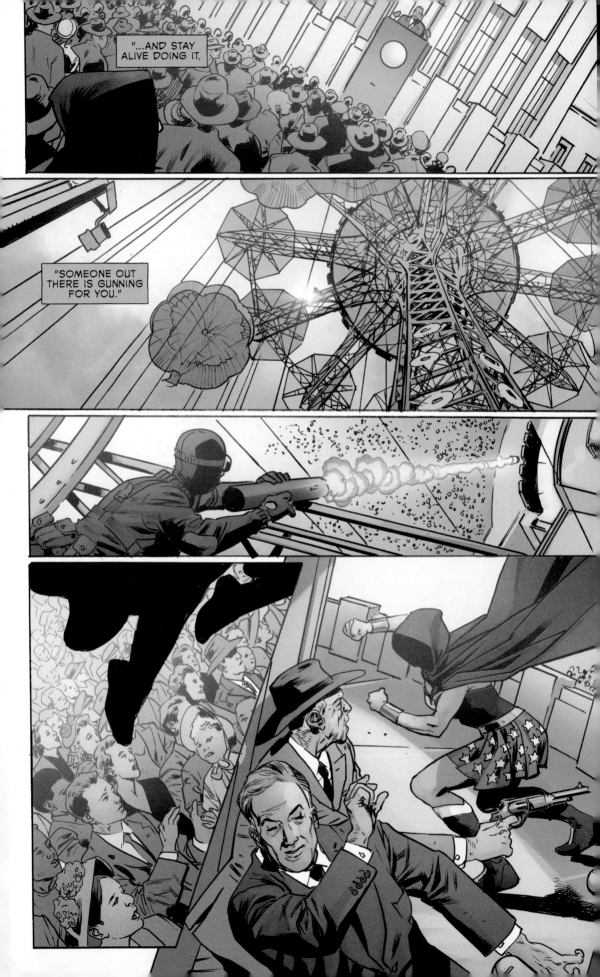

WHAT THE HELL IS GOING ON? WHO--

MR. PRESIDENT, MY NAME IS *DIANA* OF THEMYSCIRA AND I'M HERE TO WARN YOU OF A GREAT EVIL COMING...

...AND TO FIGHT *ALONGSIDE* YOU AND THE BROTHERHOOD OF MAN.

WHAT DO YOU SAY?

THAT WAS IT.

"THE MOMENT."

"SHE WAS SOMETHING BEYOND US.

"SOMETHING MORE.

"THE THINGS SHE COULD DO...

"STILL, THE FUNNY THING WAS, FOR ALL HER ABILITIES, IT WASN'T WHAT SHE COULD DO THAT CHANGED THINGS.

"NO, IT WAS WHAT SHE SAW EACH OF *US* CAPABLE OF DOING THAT CHANGED US, CHANGED EVERYTHING. SHE WAS THE FIRST SUPERHERO. AND YET...

"...IT WAS THE HEROISM SHE SAW IN EACH AND EVERY ONE OF US THAT SHINED A NEW WAY FORWARD...

"...A WAY OUT OF THE DARK."

THE BEGINNING...